ANDREW LLOYD WEBBER
SHOWSTOPPERS
Playalong *for* Trumpet

Wise Publications
part of The Music Sales Group
London/New York/Paris/Sydney/Copenhagen/Berlin/Madrid/Tokyo

Published by
Wise Publications
8/9 Frith Street, London W1D 3JB, England.

Exclusive Distributors:
Music Sales Limited
Distribution Centre, Newmarket Road, Bury St. Edmunds,
Suffolk IP33 3YB England.
Music Sales Pty Limited
120 Rothschild Avenue, Rosebery, NSW 2018, Australia.

Order No. AM91943
ISBN 0-7119-4059-2
This book © Copyright 2005 by Wise Publications.

Compiled by Nick Crispin.
Edited by Christopher Hussey and Rebecca Taylor.
Music arranged by Quentin Thomas.
Music processed by Camden Music.
Cover photography by George Taylor.
Printed in Great Britain.

CD recorded, mixed and mastered by Jonas Persson and John Rose.
Trumpet played by Tony Fisher.
Backing tracks:
'As If We Never Said Goodbye', 'Love Changes Everything', 'The Phantom Of The Opera',
'Superstar' and 'Whistle Down The Wind' arranged by Danny G.
'Close Every Door' and 'Pie Jesu' arranged by John Maul.
'Don't Cry For Me Argentina' and 'Memory' arranged by Paul Honey.
'Unexpected Song' arranged by Jeff Leach.

Trumpet Fingering Chart

MOUTHPIECE

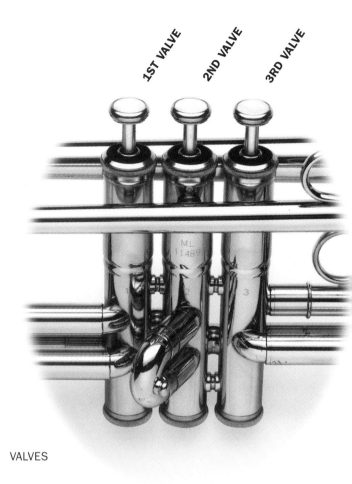

1ST VALVE   2ND VALVE   3RD VALVE

VALVES

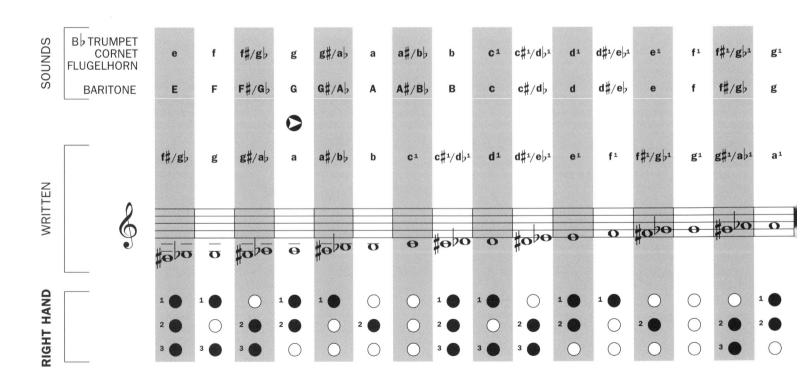

		e	f	f#/g♭	g	g#/a♭	a	a#/b♭	b	c¹	c#¹/d♭¹	d¹	d#¹/e♭¹	e¹	f¹	f#¹/g♭¹	g¹

SOUNDS — B♭ TRUMPET CORNET FLUGELHORN / BARITONE

BARITONE: E, F, F#/G♭, G, G#/A♭, A, A#/B♭, B, c, c#/d♭, d, d#/e♭, e, f, f#/g♭, g

WRITTEN: f#/g♭, g, g#/a♭, a, a#/b♭, b, c¹, c#¹/d♭¹, d¹, d#¹/e♭¹, e¹, f¹, f#¹/g♭¹, g¹, g#¹/a♭¹, a¹

RIGHT HAND

Indicates the lower limit of the best playing range

Transposition

The Bb trumpet, cornet and flugelhorn
sound a major second below the written pitch.
Rule: **Written C sounds Bb**

Written:    Sounds:

The baritone sounds a major ninth below
the written pitch. Rule: **Written C sounds Bb**

Written:    Sounds:

Pitch System

The letter names which appear at the top of the
fingering chart indicate the relative octave as well as
the name of each pitch, as shown below.

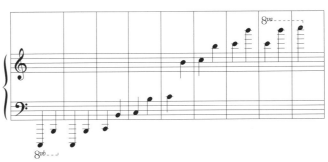

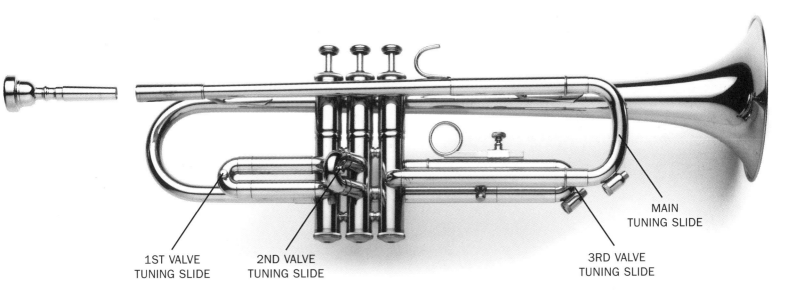

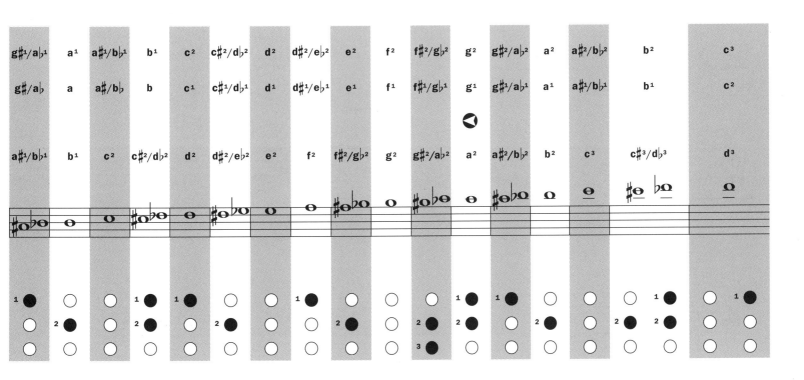

◄ Indicates the upper limit of the best playing range

As If We Never Said Goodbye

Music by Andrew Lloyd Webber
Words by Don Black & Christopher Hampton

Moderato

rit.

a tempo   piu mosso

molto allargando

a tempo

molto   *p*

rall.   **Slow**

f

ff

Close Every Door

Music by Andrew Lloyd Webber
Words by Tim Rice

Espressivo

rit. a tempo

rit.

molto rall.

Love Changes Everything

Music by Andrew Lloyd Webber
Words by Don Black & Charles Hart

Memory

Music by Andrew Lloyd Webber
Words by Trevor Nunn after T.S.Eliot

Freely (♩. = 50)

poco rall.

a tempo

poco rit.

a tempo

poco rall.   a tempo

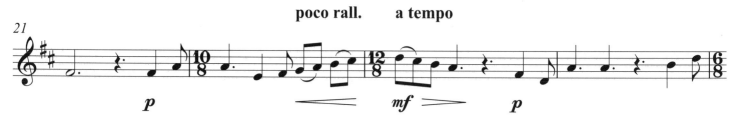

The Phantom Of The Opera

Music by Andrew Lloyd Webber
Words by Charles Hart

Allegro vivace

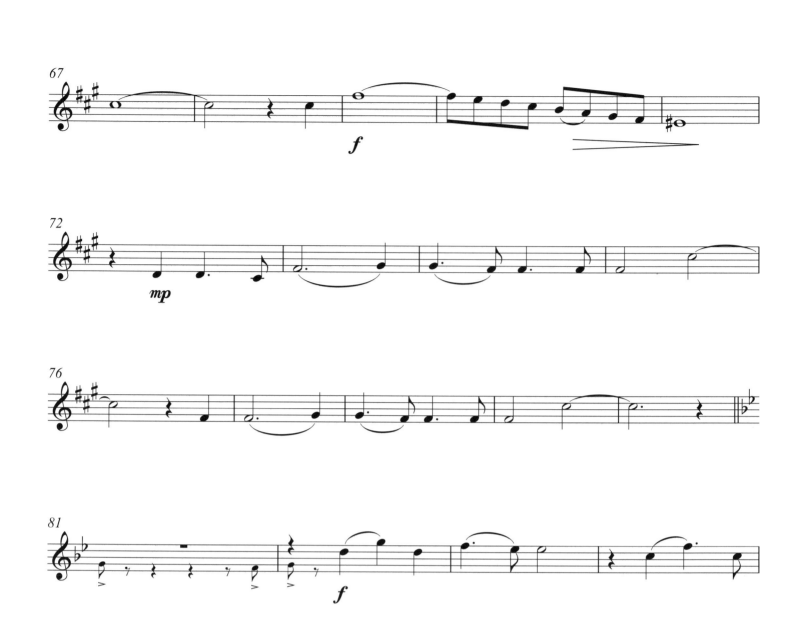

Pie Jesu

Music by Andrew Lloyd Webber

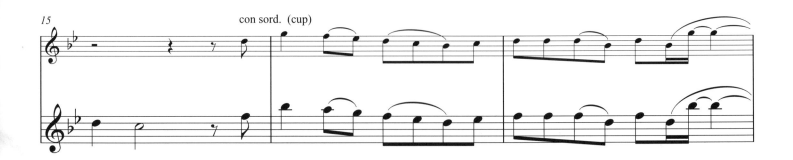

Don't Cry For Me Argentina

Music by Andrew Lloyd Webber
Words by Tim Rice

Slowly

Slow tango feel

poco rall.   **Slower**

Tempo 1º

mf

mp

Slower and freely

p

Refrain grandioso

rit.

optional
8va

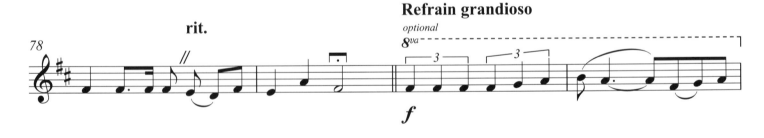

f

optional
8va

molto allargando   a tempo

mp

Superstar

Music by Andrew Lloyd Webber
Words by Tim Rice

Repeat 2 times and fade towards end

Unexpected Song

Music by Andrew Lloyd Webber
Words by Don Black

rall.   slower

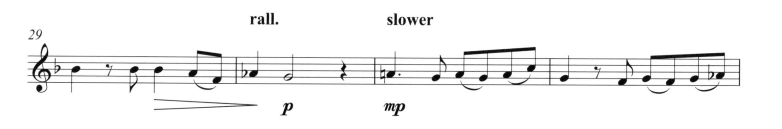

Whistle Down The Wind

Music by Andrew Lloyd Webber
Words by Jim Steinman

senza sord.